C000231976

A TEMPLAR BOOK

First published in the UK in 2022
by Templar Books,
an imprint of Bonnier Books UK,
4th Floor, Victoria House,
Bloomsbury Square, London, WC1B 4DA
Owned by Bonnier Books
Sveavägen 56, Stockholm, Sweden
www.bonnierbooks.co.uk

1 3 5 7 9 10 8 6 4 2

ISBN 978-1-80078-292-1

Edited by Ruth Symons
Designed by Collaborate
Production by Ella Holden

Printed in China

SOPHIE

Baby's First Year

This book is all about:

....

Stick photo here

Before I was born

My parents found out I was on my way on this date:

....

....

....

This is where they were when they found out:

The first people they told were:

....

....

....

My parents thought I would be a:

Boy   *Girl*

The first scan of me was on this date: ....

Here is a scan of me:

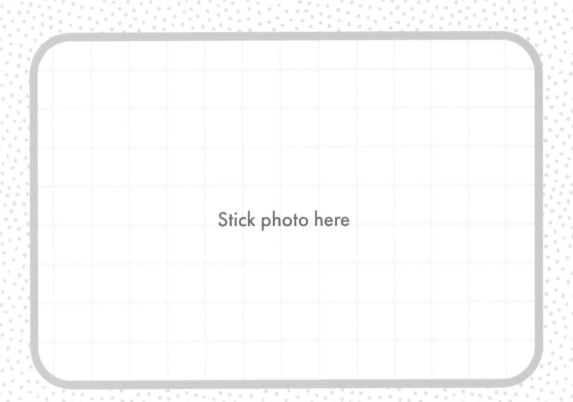

Stick photo here

Being pregnant

When she was pregnant, Mummy felt:

_____

Mummy loved to eat these foods when she was pregnant:

But she hated these foods:

These things made me kick and wriggle lots:

They first felt me kicking on:

My parents first heard my heartbeat on: -------------------------

The midwife who looked after us all was called:

My due date was:

Here is a photo of Mummy
when she was pregnant:

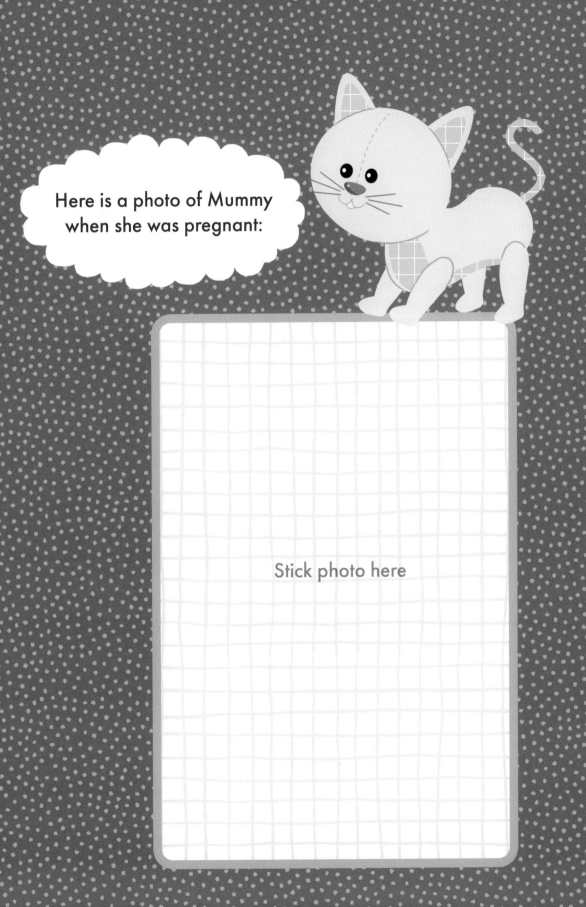

Stick photo here

Family tree

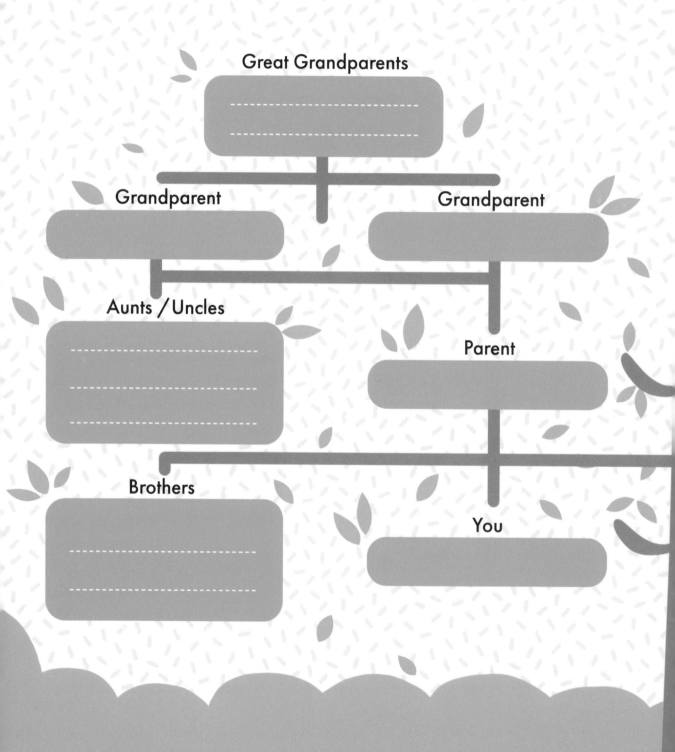

Great Grandparents

Grandparent

Grandparent

Aunts / Uncles

Parent

Brothers

You

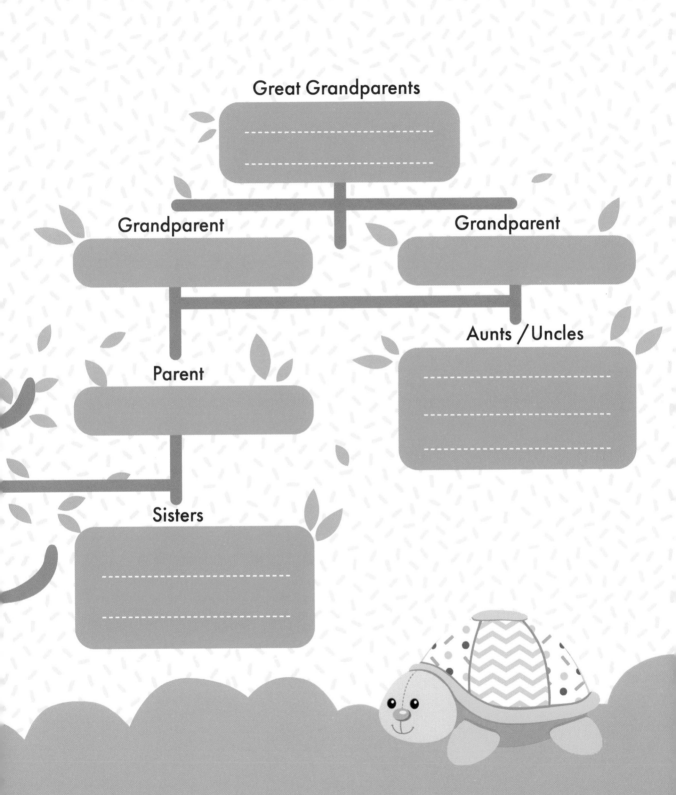

Great Grandparents

Grandparent

Grandparent

Aunts / Uncles

Parent

Sisters

The day I was born

I was born on this date:

I was born at this exact time:

I was born in this place:

It was this day of the week:

The weather was doing this:

The main news that day was:

This is the very first picture of me:

Stick photo here

All about me

I weighed this much:

_____

I was this long:

_____

My hair was this colour:

_____

My eyes were this colour:

_____

The midwife and nurses who looked after me were called:

_____

People said I looked like:

_____

Keep hospital tag here

My name

My names are:

That's because:

If I was a boy, I would have been called:

If I was a girl, I would have been called:

Gifts

My first gift was:

People also sent me:

Here are some of the people
who sent special messages:

Early days

I spent my very first night in this place:

My parents felt like this:

My first visitor was:

I came home on this day:

This is where we lived:

I had my first bath on:

Here is a photo
of me in the bath:

Stick photo here

My first footprints

My first handprints

First experiences

I went outside for the first time on this date:

We went to this place:

I smiled for the first time when I was this age:

Here is a photo of me smiling:

Stick photo here

I discovered my hands
when I was this age:

I clapped for the first time
when I was this age:

I was first poorly
when I was this age:

My first tooth came
through on this date:

On the move

I rolled over for the first time when I was this age: ....

I sat up on my own the first time when I was this age: ....

I crawled for the first time when I was this age: ....

I stood up for the first time when I was this age: ....

I took my first steps when I was this age: ....

This is where I was when I first walked: ....

My first shoes were this size: --

Here is a photo of me wearing them:

Stick photo here

Eating

The first solid food I ate was:

My reaction was:

Here is a photo of me eating:

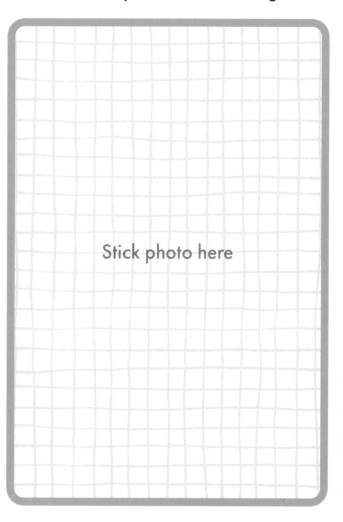

Stick photo here

These are some of the foods
I liked best:

These are some of the foods
I didn't like:

I first used a spoon when I was this age: ----------------------------

I first ate out when I was this age: -------------------------------------

This is where we went: --------------------------------

Talking

My first word was: ....

I said it on this date: ....

I first said Mama this month:

....

I first said Dada this month:

These are some of the other words I said:

....

....

....

Playtime

Some of my favourite
toys were:

Some of my favourite
books were:

I first played with Sophie la girafe when
I was ------------ months old.

I loved it when
did this:

I loved it when
did this:

One of my favourite things to do was: -------------------------------

----

New experiences

I went to some of these baby classes and groups:

....

....

....

....

These are the names of some of my friends:

....

....

....

....

Here is a photo of me with my friends:

Stick photo here

I first went on the swings when I was this age: ----------------------------

I first went swimming when I was this age: ----------------------------

I first had a haircut when I was this age: ----------------------------

Keep lock of
hair here

Holidays and special days

My first special day out was: ....

The first special celebration day after I was born was:

This is what we did:

....

....

....

....

....

The first holiday I went on was:

....

Here is a photo of us on holiday:

Stick photo here

When I was 1 month old

I was this heavy:

I was this long:

Some things I did were:

My favourite toy was:

My favourite song was:

I slept like this:

Some noises I made were:

Stick photo here

When I was 3 months old

I was this heavy:

I was this long:

Some things I did were:

My favourite toy was:

My favourite song was:

I slept like this:

Some noises I made were:

Stick photo here

When I was 6 months old

I was this heavy:

_____

I was this long:

Some things I did were:

_____

_____

My favourite toy was:

_____

_____

My favourite song was:

_____

_____

I slept like this:

_____

_____

Some noises I made were:

_____

_____

Stick photo here

When I was 9 months old

I was this heavy:

I was this long:

Some things I did were:

My favourite toy was:

My favourite song was:

I slept like this:

Some noises I made were:

Stick photo here

My first birthday!

These were the people I celebrated my birthday with:

....

....

....

We did this to celebrate:

....

....

....

....

I was given these gifts:

....

....

....

This was my favourite gift:

I ate this:

....

....

....

When I turned 1, I could say these words:

....

....

....

I was wearing this size clothing:

....

....

....

My favourite toy was:

....

I was this tall:

I weighed this much:

....

Here is a photo of me on my birthday:

Stick photo here

Getting bigger

When I turned 2 I looked like this:

Stick photo here

When I turned 3 I looked like this:

Stick photo here

When I turned 4 I looked like this:

When I turned 5 I looked like this:

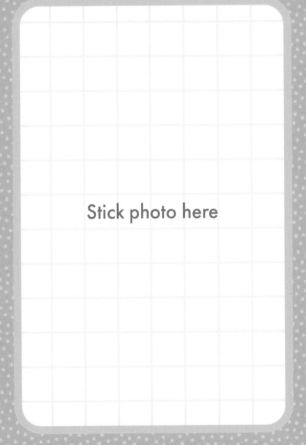

Stick photo here

Stick photo here